If...1&2

(Questions for the Game of Life)

Evelyn McFarlane & James Saywell
Illustrations by James Saywell

Villard/New York

Published in the United States by Villard Books, an imprint of Random
House, a division of Random House LLC, a Penguin Random House
Company, New York.

VILLARD BOOKS and Villard & "V" CIRCLED DESIGN are registered trademarks
of Random House LLC

IF: QUESTIONS FOR THE GAME OF LIFE and IF^2... 500 MORE
QUESTIONS FOR THE GAME OF LIFE were originally published
separately by Villard Books, an imprint of Random House, a division
of Random House LLC in 1995 and 1996 respectively.

ISBN 978-0-385-36451-5

Printed in the United States of America on acid-free paper

www.ballantinebooks.com

9 8 7 6 5 4 3 2

First Edition

If...

(Questions for the Game of Life)

Evelyn McFarlane & James Saywell
Illustrations by James Saywell

Villard/New York

If...

If is the ultimate book about fantasy. Each of its questions is meant to spark and tantalize the imagination. They are a celebration of the human spirit, which loves to dream and needs to hope, but which can also fear and even grow angry. Our ability to imagine is the remarkable gift we have been given to lead us into joy and aspiration and out of despair or sadness, because common to all of us is the idea that there could be a different world, perhaps a better one.

How many times a day do we say, "If only . . ."? If we could create the perfect life, the perfect city, the perfect home, the perfect job, the perfect mate. We all fantasize, and we all dream. We dream of perfection, money, revenge, glory, change. We fantasize about both good and evil, about winning and losing, about our past and future. Fantasies are what inspire us all; to work, marry, raise families, create, improve our world. It is why we lose ourselves in books, go to movies, watch television, go to the ballgame and on vacation. We dreamed as children and we dream now because without our fantasies we would be lost. We imagine in order to learn, to understand, to strive, to attempt, to predict, to avoid, to correct, to describe, to solve.

This book is also a game. It was born of many dinner parties and gatherings, when just to throw out a provocative question and ask for each person's answer always led to the most surprising and fascinating discussions. Every time, a kind of synergetic and addictive momentum took over as answers led to other related questions, reasons were demanded, disagreements were unleashed, conditions were imposed, other's answers were predicted, and inevitably those involved were startled by the responses, at times even their own. No matter who is present it seems to be irresistible, whether we are at a flagging party, on a long car or plane ride, among a group of students, within a family, or alone with someone very close to us. It is infectious and fascinating to watch and take part in.

Of course implicit in every question is "why?" In some sense it is like taking the pulse of a moment in time, or a group of friends, to see what we believe in; to see what world we envision. Whether they are read randomly or in sequence, the responses these questions elicit can lead to extraordinary offshoots; other related questions will occur, and variations on these, and attached caveats and conditions "customize" the original list depending on who is there to play. Because everybody, old or young, fat or thin, intelligent or not, from one culture or another, has the ability and inclination to wonder.

And so, aside from the truths that are revealed, the contemplation that is provoked, the confidence or anxiety that surfaces, the self-knowledge that results, or the understanding that might be gained, above all we hope that asking these questions inspires optimism, since no matter who or what we really are, we share the ability to travel together the unpredictable journey of the imagination, which leads us through the wonderful game of life.

If...

If you were to be granted one wish, what would it be?

If you could spend one whole night alone with anyone in the world who is currently alive, who would you select?

If you could spend one whole night alone with anyone in history, who would you choose?

If you could physically transport yourself to any place in the world at this moment, where would you go?

If you could have lived through any war in history (without actually fighting in it), which would it be?

↦ ═◆═ ↤

If you could eliminate any one type of insect permanently from the earth, what would you get rid of?

↦ ═◆═ ↤

If you had to eliminate a single type of animal forevermore, which would you choose?

If you could have an elegant dinner alone with anyone presently alive, whether you know them or not, who would you want it to be?

If you could alter one physical characteristic of your mate, what would you change?

If you could dine alone with anyone from any period in history, which person would it be?

If you could, in retrospect, change one thing about your childhood, what would it be?

If you could have any room in the world become your bedroom from now on, which room would you choose?

If you could change one thing in the world right now, what would you alter?

＋―❉❖❉―＋

If you had to assassinate one famous person who is alive right now, who would it be, and how would you do it?

＋―❉❖❉―＋

If you could permanently alter one thing about your physical appearance, what would you change?

＋―❉❖❉―＋

If you could have stopped aging at any point in your life up to the present, how old would you want to remain?

8

If you could inherit a comfortable home in any city in the world that you could use but not sell, where would you want it to be?

If you could inherit a vacation home anywhere in the world in which you could spend one month a year, but that you could never sell, where would it be?

If you could suddenly possess an extraordinary talent in one of the arts, what would you like it to be?

If you could be instantly fluent in one other language that you currently do not read or speak, which would it be?

If you could have permanent possession of any single object in the world, what would you want it to be?

If you could have had the starring role in one film already made, which movie would you pick?

If you could return for one year to one age in your life, knowing what you know now, to relive that year as you wish, which year would you go back to?

If you had to identically repeat any single year of your life to date, without changing a thing, which year would you relive?

If you could be sculpted by any artist in history, who would you choose?

—————— ≡♦≡ ——————

If you were to have your entire wardrobe designed for you by a single clothing designer for the rest of your life, who would you select?

—————— ≡♦≡ ——————

If you were to be stranded forever on a desert island and could have only one book to read, which would you want?

—————— ≡♦≡ ——————

If you could say one sentence to the current pope, what would it be?

11

If you could have one person from history live his or her full life over again, starting now, who would you pick?

If you could have personally witnessed one event in history, what would you want to have seen?

If one of your parents was to be a famous person from any time in history, who would you want them to be?

If you could receive one small package this very moment, who would it be from and what would be in it?

12

If you could own one painting from any collection in the world but were not allowed to sell it, which work of art would you select?

If you could have chosen your own first name, other than your current one, what would it be?

If you could have seduced one person that you knew in your lifetime (but didn't), who would you select?

If you were instantly able to play one musical instrument perfectly that you never have played before, what would it be?

If you were to be stranded forever on a tropical island with one platonic friend only, in whose company would you want to spend the rest of your days?

If you had to live the rest of your life in a place that you have never lived in before, where would you live?

If you could keep only one article of clothing you currently own and the rest were to be thrown out, what would you keep?

If you had to lose one of your five senses, which would you give up?

If you were to have one famous person alive or from history stranded with you on an island forevermore, who would you want it to be?

If you could kill the pet of anybody you know, whose pet would it be?

If you were to be recognized by posterity for one thing, what would you like to be known for?

If you could have said one sentence to Hitler while he was alive, what would you have said?

15

If you had to choose the color that describes you most accurately, which color would it be?

If you had to convert to a different religion, which would you choose?

If you were to drown in a liquid other than water, what would you want it to be?

If you could reverse one sports call in history, which one would it be?

If you had to name the most terrifying moment of your life so far, what would it be?

＊ ＝◆＝ ＊

If you had to be homeless for one year, where would you want to be?

＊ ＝◆＝ ＊

If you could have one street or square or park in any city or town renamed after you, which one would you select and exactly what would the name be?

If you could be guaranteed one thing in life besides money, what would you ask for?

If you could have one person alive today call you for advice, who would you want it to be?

———— ✦ ————

If you could have any person from any time in history call you for advice, and they were to listen to what you told them, who would you want to hear from?

———— ✦ ————

If you could easily visit one known planet, which one would you go to?

If you could have been the author of any single book already written, which book would you want to have penned?

If you could have any one specific power over other people, what would it be?

If you had to lose everyone you know in a tragic accident except one person, who would you choose to survive?

If you could have one meal from your past exactly as it was, which would you repeat?

If you could become famous for doing something that you don't currently do, what would it be?

If you could only keep one of your five senses, which would you save?

＋—— ▆◆▆ ——＋

If you could have lived during one period of time in past history, when and where would it be?

＋—— ▆◆▆ ——＋

If one by one, you had to place each of the people with you right now in another period of history that you think suits them best, when and where would you place them?

＋—— ▆◆▆ ——＋

If you had to describe the saddest thing that ever happened to you, what would you talk about?

If you had to spend one year alone in the wilderness, where would you go?

— ⚡ —

If you had to work in one type of factory for the remainder of your days but could choose which kind, what would you pick?

If you could possess one supernatural ability, what would it be?

— ⚡ —

If you had to paint your entire home, inside and out, a single color other than white, what color would you pick?

If you could have any single writer from history write your biography, who would it be?

If you could have one current writer write your biography, who would you pick?

If you could forever eliminate one specific type of prejudice from the earth, which would it be?

If you could transport everyone you are with at this moment to another place, where would you all go?

22

If your home were to be totally destroyed by fire but you could save just one thing, what would it be?

If you were to have your friends, in private, attribute a single quality to you, what would you want it to be?

If you had to kill someone you know, who would it be, and how would you do it?

If a photograph of one part of your body were to be used in an advertisement, which part would you want to be used, and for what product or service?

If you could bring back any past leader of your country to run the country again, who would you want?

If you could own any building in existence, which would you pick?

If you could choose exactly what you will eat and drink for your last meal before death, what would the menu consist of?

If you could own any one existing sculpture from anywhere in the world, but not the right to ever sell it, which one would you want?

If you could make a gift of one thing to any single person alive today, who would it be, what would you give them, and how would you present it to them?

+—⟨◆⟩—+

If you could have composed any single piece of music that already exists, which would you choose?

+—⟨◆⟩—+

If you were invited to join one current musical group, which group would you want to be a member of, and what instrument would you play?

+—⟨◆⟩—+

If you were to receive any existing public award, what award would you like to win?

25

If you could decide how to spend your last day alive, what would you do?

If you could decide what will be written on your gravestone, what would you have inscribed?

If you had to choose the single most valuable thing you ever learned, what would it be?

If you were kidnapped and allowed to telephone one person for one minute only, who would you call?

26

If you could enact one law in your country that does not currently exist, what would it be?

—— ⋈ ——

If you could own only one thing for the rest of your life, what would you choose?

If you could be the current world champion in any one sport, which sport would it be?

—— ⋈ ——

If you could spend a weekend in any hotel in the world with all expenses paid, which hotel would you choose?

If you could cast an actor now alive to play you in a new film, what kind of film would it be and who would you choose?

＋┄ ≣✦≣ ┄＋

If an actor no longer alive were to play you in a film, who would you cast in the role?

If you could have your portrait painted by any painter in history, to whom would you give the commission?

＋┄ ≣✦≣ ┄＋

If you were given one hour to spend an unlimited amount of money in any store in the world, where would it be?

If you could say one sentence to the leader of the country you are presently in, what would you say?

If you had to choose the best advertising campaign ever created, which one would it be?

If you could have been any person from history, who would you want to have been?

If you could have a song written about you, what musician would you want to compose it, who would perform it, and what would it be called?

If you had to donate everything you own to a charity that you have never given to previously, which charity would you give to?

⋯⋯ ▰◆▰ ⋯⋯

If you could work for any person in the world, who would it be, and what job would you want?

⋯⋯ ▰◆▰ ⋯⋯

If you could discover one item that belonged to someone in history, whose would it be, and what would it be?

⋯⋯ ▰◆▰ ⋯⋯

If you could "uninvent" one thing in the world so that it would no longer exist, what would you choose?

If you were to be executed tomorrow but could decide the method, how would you prefer to go?

If you could play any position on your favorite sports team, what would it be?

—·— ⬄ —·—

If you could have a year any place in the world, all expenses paid, where would you go?

—·— ⬄ —·—

If you could see only one movie ever again, what film would you choose?

If you had to choose the title of your autobiography, what would it be?

If you could have only one piece of furniture in your house, what would you want it to be?

If you could have changed one thing about your first sexual experience, what would it be?

If you had to sleep with two famous people simultaneously, who would you choose?

If you could destroy a single tape or CD that your mate plays, what would it be?

If you could read the private diary of someone you know personally, whose diary would you read?

If you could read the diary of one person you don't know personally, whose would it be?

If you were on trial and someone you know (who is not a lawyer) had to act as your legal representative, who would you want to defend you?

If you could change one of your personality traits, what would it be?

If you could adopt one personality trait from someone you know, what would you take, and from whom?

If you could have a romance with any fictional character, who would it be?

If you could have one person you know be your slave for one month, who would you choose?

34

If you could have avoided living one year from your past, which year would you like to have eliminated?

——— ≡◆≡ ———

If you could have the home phone number of anyone in the world, whose would it be, and what would you say to them?

If you could commit one crime without being caught, what crime would you commit?

——— ≡◆≡ ———

If you were kidnapped and could bring along only one personal possession, what would you take?

35

If you could be the parent of one famous person, who would you want it to be?

If you could ensure that your children never have one experience that you have had, what would it be?

If you could eat one food in any quantity for the rest of your life with no ill affects whatsoever, what food would you choose?

If you had to eliminate one season permanently (spring, summer, autumn, or winter), which one would go?

If you were going to initiate a new charity, what would be its mission and who would it benefit?

***

If you could have been vice-president to any American president, which president would you choose?

***

If you could "unknow" one thing you know, what would it be?

***

If you could have one entire country "depopulated" as your private property, which country would you take as your own?

37

If you could have a secret camera in any one room in the world, what room would you put it in?

If you had to lose one of your limbs, which one would you sacrifice?

If you could only keep one of your limbs, which would you choose to keep?

If you were to have sex with two people simultaneously that you have known from your own past, who would you pick?

38

If you were to be the personal valet of any one man or woman from history, who would you want to work for?

If you could hire any architect alive or from history to design your dream house, who would you pick, and where would you build it?

If you could have invented anything from history, what would you pick?

If you could invent something that currently does not exist, what would it be?

If you could have been the first person to discover any part of the world, what place would you want to have found?

If you could have any music group alive today play at your birthday party, which group would you hire?

If you could have any music group that no longer exists play at your birthday party, who would you want?

If you could have a secret hideaway to escape to with a lover, where would it be?

If you were to cast the two romantic leads of a new film with any actors alive, who would you pick?

$\leftarrow\!\!+\!\!\rule[0.5ex]{2em}{0.4pt}\!\!+\!\!\rightarrow$

If you could choose the way you will die, how would you want it to happen?

$\leftarrow\!\!+\!\!\rule[0.5ex]{2em}{0.4pt}\!\!+\!\!\rightarrow$

If you could foresee a single day of your future in its entirety, what date would you select?

$\leftarrow\!\!+\!\!\rule[0.5ex]{2em}{0.4pt}\!\!+\!\!\rightarrow$

If you had to have fought in any war in history, which would you have fought in?

If you could ask God any single question, what would it be?

If you could be one article of clothing, what would you be, and who would you want to belong to?

If you had to be someone's body part, what would you be, and on whose body?

If you were to be rescued from a desert island, by whom would you want to be rescued?

42

If you had to eat the same meal for the rest of your life, morning, noon, and night, without worrying about nutrition, what would you eat?

If you could live the life of any fictional character, which character would it be?

If you could have been any past president of the United States, who would you have been?

If you could have one person from history work for you as your personal assistant, who would it be?

43

If you could have the mind of someone you know but remain in your own body, whose brain would you take?

If you could have the mind of someone from history and remain in your own body, whose would you choose?

If you could coach any current sports team professionally, which would you choose?

If you had to name the single most regrettable thing about your country's history, what would it be?

If you could star in a love scene with any living actor, who would you want to act with, and where would you want it filmed?

— ≡✦≡ —

If you could have survived any historic disaster, which would you choose?

— ≡✦≡ —

If you could discover that something you thought was true was actually false, what would you wish it to be?

— ≡✦≡ —

If you could leave flowers on any one person's grave every week whether you knew them or not, who would it be?

If you could be invisible for one hour, where would you go and what would you do?

If you could relive one romantic date from high school just as it was, which would it be?

If you could relive one romantic date from high school as you would like it to have been, which would you choose?

If you had to give up all sexual activity for one year, how much money would you demand (minimum) in return?

If you had to keep one part of your mate's body permanently in the freezer, what part would you save?

If you were the sole survivor of a plane crash with everyone present and had to choose someone to eat in order to survive, who would you select?

If you could eliminate one hereditary characteristic from your family, what would it be?

If you could be a student of any university in the world right now, where would you enroll?

If you could host a dinner party in any room in the world (without having to clean up), where would you want to have it?

If you could host a dinner party inviting any four people from history, who would you invite and where would the party take place?

If you were to be married to someone who is famous now, who would you pick to be your new spouse?

If you had to be married to someone famous from the past who is no longer alive, who would you like it to be?

If you had to have sex with someone that you know personally who is not of your sexually preferred gender, who would you select?

If you could arrange a rock concert with any three musicians or groups to play on the same bill, who would you invite?

If you could relive one single day from your past exactly as it was the first time, what day would you choose to experience all over again?

If you could wake up tomorrow to learn that the major newspaper headlines were about you, what would you want them to say?

49

If you could eliminate one day from your past so that you had never had to live through it, which day would you erase?

If you could go back in time, as yourself, to live for one year at any point in history, what year would you choose, and where would you go?

If you could have had one composer from history write a symphony for you, who would it be?

If you were to receive a letter today from anyone you have known during your lifetime, who would it be from and what would it say?

50

If you could have a telegram from one famous person now alive, who would it be from, and what would it say?

⚜

If you could have a telegram from one person from history, who would it be from and what would it say?

If one part of your body was to become a religious relic, which part would you like it to be?

⚜

If you were to be successful in another profession, what would you want to do?

51

If you could have been the architect of any one building in history, which building would you choose?

If you could have directed any film in history, what movie would it be?

— ✦ —

If you had to spend all of your vacations for the rest of your life in the same place, where would you go?

— ✦ —

If you were stranded on a desert island and could have with you only one object you currently own, what would you take?

If you won a lottery, what is the first thing you would do?

If you could have a secret listening device in any one room in the world, which room would you like it to be in?

If you had to inhabit the body of someone you know personally while keeping your own mind, whose body would you take?

If you could be a member of any club or association in the world, what would it be?

53

If you were given $5,000 to spend in one store in the world, where would you do your shopping?

If you could steal one thing in the world, other than money, without getting caught, what would you take?

If you could be the lover of any person alive other than your current lover, who would you pick?

If you could have been a lover of any person in history, who would you choose?

If you had to die in one of history's disasters, which one would you pick?

***

If you could take revenge on any person you have ever known, who would it be, why do they deserve it, and how would you do it?

***

If you were to perform in the circus, what would you do?

If you could master one type of cuisine, which one would you choose?

If you could be master chef in any restaurant in the world, where would you choose to cook?

If you could ensure that your child has one experience that you have had yourself, what would you want it to be?

If you could have a free telephone line to any one person in the world, who would it be?

If you could retract one lie you have told in your life, which would it be?

If you were stranded on a desert island and could have only one piece of music to listen to, what would it be?

If you were to die in a public place, exactly what spot would you choose?

If you were elected to be leader of a foreign country tomorrow, what country would you want it to be and what would be your first official act?

If you had to have one piece of music softly playing in your mind for the rest of your life, what would you want it to be?

If you had to have one family member (besides your spouse) witness your next sexual act, who would you pick?

—+—— ⚏✦⚏ ——+—

If you could see anyone alive fully naked, who would you select?

—+—— ⚏✦⚏ ——+—

If you could see one famous person from history fully naked, who would it be?

—+—— ⚏✦⚏ ——+—

If you could be any sports figure now alive, who would you want to be?

If you were to give one person you know an award for something, who would it be, and for what?

If you had to choose someone with you right now to be president of the United States, who would you want it to be?

If you could become rich doing one thing that you currently don't do, what would you want it to be?

If you were to be a machine, what machine would you be?

If you could erase any one murder from history, which would it be?

----⚍⊹⚍----

If you had to change citizenship, which country would you want to become a citizen of?

----⚍⊹⚍----

If you could be married anywhere in the world, where would the wedding take place?

If you could be buried anywhere, where would it be?

If you could ensure one single personality trait in your children, what would you want it to be?

If you could run any single company, institution, or organization in the world, which would you choose?

If you had to select any single manmade object that best represents your personality, what would it be?

If you could gain total memory of one year of your life so far, which year would you pick?

If you could overthrow any government in the world, which one would you replace?

If you were to have a one-night stand with a current world leader, who would you choose?

If you were to bear the child of a famous person alive today, whose child would you like to have?

If you could have borne the child of a famous person no longer living, who would you choose?

If you could choose any historic figure to read your eulogy, who would you want to do it?

If you could call any person from history for advice tonight, who would you prefer to talk to?

＊＋☰◆☰＋＊

If you could put anyone in prison, who would you lock up?

＊＋☰◆☰＋＊

If you could undo one sexual encounter in your life so that it never happened, which one would it be?

If you could choose the music at your own funeral, what would it be, and who would play it?

If you had to sleep with someone you despise in exchange for one thing, what is it that you would demand?

If you had to spy on your own country for another country, which nation would you do it for?

If you had to name your single worst fear, what would it be?

If you had to describe the single worst thing a friend could do to you, what would it be?

If you were to invent an award to give to one commercial company, which one would you award, and for what?

If you could resolve any single dispute, anywhere in the world, what would you solve?

If you could be a contestant on any game show, which would you like to be on?

If you could read the mind of anyone you know, who would it be?

If you could read the mind of someone famous, who would it be?

If you could dance any one dance perfectly, which dance would you choose?

If you could be the editor of any single magazine, what publication would you pick?

66

If you were elected to be the leader of the United States tomorrow, what would be your first act?

If you could eliminate one thing you do each day in the bathroom so that you never had to do it again, what would it be?

If you had to have your mate get a part of their body pierced, exactly where would you want it to be?

If you could only hear one voice that you are familiar with for the rest of your life from the mouth of all people, whose would it be?

If you could serve in one capacity in the military (in which you haven't already served), what would you want to do?

⊷ ⚎✦⚏ ↤

If you could eliminate forevermore one cause of death on earth, what would it be?

If you had to choose the best book in history, which book would get the prize?

⊷ ⚎✦⚏ ↤

If you had to choose the worst book ever written, what would it be?

If you could use only one cosmetic item for the rest of your life, what would you choose?

·—·—≡◆≡—·—·

If you could cure any disease, which would it be?

·—·—≡◆≡—·—·

If you could be the owner of any current team in professional sports, which one would you want?

·—·—≡◆≡—·—·

If you had to eliminate one odor from the earth, which one would you get rid of?

If you had to permanently give up your children to the care of someone you know, who would you wish it to be?

━━ ✦ ━━

If you had to give up your children to the care of someone famous, who would you pick?

━━ ✦ ━━

If you were to select a food that best describes your character, what food would it be?

━━ ✦ ━━

If you could arrange a jam session with any three musicians in history, who would you include?

If you could invent one new home appliance, what would it do?

�

If you were to be someone's personal computer, whose would you like to be?

If you were to be a news correspondent posted to any foreign country, where would you like to go?

⟢ ≡ ◆ ≡ ⟣

If you had to choose a time in history when overall things were worse than any other single time, when would you say it was?

71

If you could take away the vocal chords of any person, who would it be?

--- ≍✦≍ ---

If you had to have one platonic friend witness your next sexual act, who would you ask?

If you could be a guest on any television talk show, which would it be?

--- ≍✦≍ ---

If you were suddenly naked in front of everyone at work, what would you say to them?

If you could keep only one thing that is in your bathroom right now, as the only thing in there forever, what would you save?

If you could have prevented one event in history, what event would you eliminate?

If you had to rename your hometown, what would you call it?

If you could teach your children only one lesson in life, what would it be?

73

If you had to be a member of another family you know, which family would you join?

—⊷ ⊵✦⊴ ⊶—

If you had to cast living actors to play each of the people with you right now in a new film, who would you choose to play each person?

—⊷ ⊵✦⊴ ⊶—

If you had to choose the worst work of art ever created, what would you choose?

—⊷ ⊵✦⊴ ⊶—

If you had to choose the greatest work of art in history, what would you say is the best?

74

If you had the chance to make one purchase that you have passed up in your lifetime, what would it be?

If you had to describe your idea of the perfect mate, how would you do it?

If you could have been the producer of any single television show or series, which one would you pick?

If you could own any single newspaper in the world, which one would you pick?

If you could choose any six people to be the pallbearers at your funeral, who would you choose?

＋—＝◆＝—＋

If you had to repeat your exact life over again exactly as it was, from any age, what age would you go back to?

If you could find one thing, besides money, in your family attic, what would you want to discover?

＋—＝◆＝—＋

If you could go back to any age and start a different life, what age would that be?

If you had to eliminate a single art form from the earth henceforth and forevermore, which one would you get rid of?

—— ⚬ ——

If you had to name the single most important quality of a good mate, what would it be?

—— ⚬ ——

If the world could henceforth have only one single art form, what do you think it should be?

—— ⚬ ——

If you had been the original designer of one existing corporate logo, which one would you select?

77

If you could wear only one color, besides white or black, for the rest of your life, what would you wear?

If you had to eat in only one restaurant for the rest of your life, which one would you choose?

If you had to be represented by an object in your home, what would you choose?

If you could have changed any one thing about the death of one of your relatives, what would you alter?

If you had been the reporter to have broken one news event during your lifetime, what would you like it to have been?

----- ≡◆≡ -----

If you could have any type of fresh cut flowers delivered to your home every week, what one type would you pick?

----- ≡◆≡ -----

If you had to be the underwear of someone famous, who would you choose to wear you?

If you could have refereed one sports match in history, which one would you pick?

If you could put a new tattoo on someone you know, who would you pick, what would it be, and where would you put it?

If you could make someone else live one moment from your own life, who would you select, and what moment?

If you could keep only one home appliance, which would you keep?

If you were to be reincarnated as an animal, what kind would you want to be?

If you could ask a single question of a dead relative, what would it be and of whom would you ask it?

If you could have changed one thing about your parents while you were a child, what would it have been?

If you had to have a personal friend redecorate your house, who would you pick to do it?

If you could give a single piece of advice to the film industry in Hollywood, what would you say?

81

If you had to rename each of the people you are with right now, what would you call each of them?

—— ≡✦≡ ——

If you had to marry someone that you presently know un-romantically, and spend the rest of your life as their spouse, who would you choose?

—— ≡✦≡ ——

If you had to choose one country in the world other than the United States to become the only superpower of the twenty-first century, which country would you pick?

—— ≡✦≡ ——

If you had to choose one person currently in the U.S. government to control the nuclear forces instead of the president, who would it be?

If you could choose both major candidates for the next United States presidential race, what two people would you pick?

—·—·— ⚔ —·—·—

If you could have worked for anyone in history, in your own field, who would you choose?

—·—·— ⚔ —·—·—

If you could have been the person who discovered any country in history, which country would you like to have been the first to find?

If you had to cancel one hour of the day, every day, which hour would you eliminate?

If you could go back in time, as yourself, to observe any single event from history, what would you want to witness?

If you were to choose a musical instrument that best describes your character, what would it be?

If you had to exchange one physical attribute with someone in the room, who would you pick, and what would you exchange with them?

If you had to cancel one month of the year forevermore, so that period of time no longer existed, which month would go?

If you could choose one new symbol for your family crest, what would it be?

If you could do any job in the world for one day, what would it be?

If you could be anywhere in history for one day, as someone famous from that time, where would you like to be, when, and as who?

If you had to choose the best television show ever made, which one would you pick?

If you could have been any sports figure from history, who would you want to have been?

If you could change one thing about your life, what would it be?

If you had to choose the prize for the best movie in history, what film would win?

If you had to pick the worst movie in history, which one would get the dubious honor?

If you could practice only one of the principle vices hence-forth, which one would you stick with?

If you could have discovered one medical cure in history, which one would you choose?

If you could have sued any one person in your life, who would it be, and for what?

If you could have been a jury member in any court case in history, which trial would you choose?

If you had to murder someone, how would you do it?

———— ❊ ————

If you had to commit suicide by jumping from a tall height, where would you do it?

If you could choose the very last thing you will see before death, what would it be?

———— ❊ ————

If you had to trade houses with someone you know, who would it be?

88

If you had to have been any dictator or tyrant in history, which one would you choose to have been?

·—· ⊫✦⊨ ·—·

If you could add one sentence to the U.S. Constitution, what would it say?

·—· ⊫✦⊨ ·—·

If you could bomb one building in the world without hurting any people, which would you blow up?

·—· ⊫✦⊨ ·—·

If you could be the author of any one quotation from history, what words would you like to have uttered?

If you had to confess to one crime you have already committed, what would you confess to?

If you could choose, from what you own right now, what clothes to be buried in when you die, what would you wear?

If you had to describe the worst job interview in your life, what job would it have been for?

If you could have hit any homerun in baseball history, which one would you choose?

90

If you were to be any famous person's personal masseuse, whose would you like to be?

If you could give anonymous advice to any one person about their appearance, who would it be, and what would you say?

If you could be on the cover of any magazine next month, which magazine would you want it to be, and what would the caption say?

If you had to pick the worst meal you've ever eaten, what would it be?

If everything in the world had to have the same odor, what scent would you want it to be?

＊＊＊

If you could give your parents one gift, what would you give them?

If you were to receive one honorary degree in your lifetime, which university would you prefer, and for what accomplishment?

＊＊＊

If you could have given one speech in history, which one would you pick?

If you could have been on the United States Supreme Court for any single case in its history, which would you select?

If you could physically strike one person from your past (that you didn't), who would you hit, and where?

If you could change one election result from the past so that the loser had won, which one would it be?

If you had to die from something other than old age, how would you prefer to go?

If you had to name the worst job in the world, what would it be?

⊱─━⊰◆⊱━─⊰

If you could own the entire wardrobe of any one television character, from the show they're on, whose clothes would you want?

⊱─━⊰◆⊱━─⊰

If you could cancel one vacation you have taken, lose all memory of it, and get your money back, what vacation would you choose?

⊱─━⊰◆⊱━─⊰

If you had to choose the worst work experience you've ever had, what would you pick?

94

If you could cancel forever a single thing you have to do every day other than your job, what would it be?

⊷ ⊨◈⊨ ⊶

If you had to go tonight to be tattooed, where on your body would you have it done and what image would you select?

⊷ ⊨◈⊨ ⊶

If you could realize a dream that you have had while asleep, what dream would you pick?

If you could choose only one color and image for your country's new flag, what would it look like?

If you had to identify the worst hotel room you have ever stayed in, where was it?

If you had to name the most important invention in history, what would win?

If you had to describe the best kiss you've ever had, how would you describe it?

If your house were to be haunted by the ghost of one person from history, who would you wish it to be?

If you had to choose the best song ever composed, which one would it be?

❖

If you had to choose the worst song ever composed, which one would you pick?

❖

If you had to change your race, what would you want to be?

❖

If you had to select the most beautiful face in history, whose face would you pick?

If you had to pick the worst sexual experience of your life, what would it be?

If you could solve one unsolved crime, which one would you solve?

If you were to be renamed after someone from history, whose name would you want?

If you could accomplish only one thing in the rest of your life, what would it be?

If you could have the sex life of any person from history, but remain yourself, who would you choose?

––––– ≡◊≡ –––––

If you could have anyone's eyes in the world, whose eyes would you want?

If you could completely eliminate one of your pet peeves, what would you get rid of?

––––– ≡◊≡ –––––

If you could win any competition in the world, what would it be for?

If you had to choose the worst telephone call you've ever had, what call was it?

If you had to choose the best telephone call you've ever had, which was it?

If you could have the hair of someone you know, whose would you take?

If you had to serve a life sentence in jail for one crime, what crime would you commit?

100

If you just learned that you had exactly one year to live, what would you do with your remaining time?

If you were to have only one of the prime virtues, which one would you want to possess?

If you could break one current world sports record, which one would it be?

If you had to recall the worst date you've ever been on, which one was it?

If you were to permanently give up sex for one thing other than money, what would you do it for?

If you could tell your boss one thing with complete impunity, what would you say?

If you could have prevented one natural disaster that actually happened, what would it be?

If you could hold one position in current government, what would you want to do?

If your plane was about to crash and you had time to write one quick note, to whom would you write, and what would you say?

* ⚎ *

If you were to adopt an orphan from another country, which country would the child come from?

If you were to pick a moment in history when, all things considered, the world was better off, which would it be?

* ⚎ *

If you could change one thing to make life easier for your own gender, what would you change?

If you were allowed to eat only one vegetable for the rest of your life, which one would it be?

If you could change the ending of any book ever written, which one would you pick and how would you change it?

If you had to spend one weekend alone in a single store but could remove nothing, which store would you pick?

If you could referee or judge one sport as a permanent job, which would you choose?

If you could give a single piece of advice to the automobile industry, what would you tell them?

--- ❈ ---

If you had to choose someone to sleep with your mate, who would you pick?

--- ❈ ---

If you had to sacrifice your own life for one thing, what would it be?

--- ❈ ---

If you had to repeat one alcohol or drug experience you've had, which one would you relive?

105

If you could see through the clothes of any one person at all times, who would it be?

If you could call any living person to ask for advice tonight, who would you call?

If you could recover one thing you've lost in your lifetime, what would you wish to find?

If you could memorize one book from history in its entirety, which book would you want it to be?

If you could make a sequel to any movie you have ever seen, which one would it be?

If you were given a yacht today, what would you name it?

If you were given a racehorse, what would you name it?

If you had to name the best purchase you've ever made, which one would you choose?

If you could spend one year looking for one thing in the world, what would you search for?

If you had written one song from this century yourself, which would you like to have written?

If you could have been told one thing that you weren't told when you were a teenager, what would you like to have heard?

If you were sentenced to spend the rest of your life in a prison cell with one person you know, who would you take?

If you could pick one famous person to be your neighbor, who would you have next door to you?

If you could live on any one street in the world, which address would you choose?

If you could sing any one song beautifully and perfectly, which one would you pick?

If you were going to turn to crime to support yourself from now on, what kind of criminal would you become?

109

If you could occupy the world described in a novel, which would you choose?

If you could change one thing about your home, what would you make different?

If you could make one fairytale or fable come true with yourself in it, which would you pick?

If you could teach a person any single thing, who and what would you choose?

If you had to cancel one day of the week forever, which day would go?

If you could break one world's record for anything other than sports, what would it be?

If you had to choose the worst home you've ever lived in, which one was it?

If you could be the only one to hear the confession of one criminal from history, who would it be?

If you had to choose the most important single event of this century, what would win the honor?

━━━ ✦ ━━━

If you could leave a time capsule the size of a microwave oven to be found centuries from now, what would you put inside it?

If you were asked what to put in a new breakfast cereal box as a gimmick, what would you pick?

━━━ ✦ ━━━

If you had to secretly dispose of a dead body, how would you do it?

If you could be forgiven for one thing in your life, what would you choose?

If you had to predict the most important development of the twenty-first century, what do you think it will be?

If you could only have sex once more in your life, when would you do it, with whom, and where?

If you could romantically kiss someone that you never have, who would you want it to be?

If you could keep your mate but have the rest of the world populated by only one gender, which would it be?

If you could have a voodoo doll that functioned for one person you know, who would that person be, and what would you use it for?

If you could change one thing about your city or town or neighborhood, what would you alter?

If you could firebomb any store or business, which would you do it to?

114

If you had to pick the most important quality for a leader of your country, what would it be?

If you could change the ending to one movie you have seen, which one would it be, and how would you reshoot it?

If you could reverse the effects of any one environmental problem that we are currently faced with, what problem would you choose to mend?

If you could, in retrospect, have purchased a large quantity of stock the day it was first issued, which one would it have been?

If you had to choose the single biggest mistake you have made in life so far, what would it be?

—————

If you could throw a party in any existing interior space in the world, where would you have it?

—————

If you could arrange for any two singers to record a duet together, which two would you pick, and what song would you have them sing?

If you had to describe your worst medical experience, what would it be?

If you could give anonymous advice to one set of parents you know about how they are raising their kids, who would it be and what would you tell them?

If you could go back in time just long enough to tell the founding fathers of America one thing, what would you tell or warn them of?

If you could eliminate one habit your mate has, what would you have them stop doing?

If you had to spend one weekend alone in a single public building or institution, which building would you choose?

117

If you could have one current politician removed from office, who would you get rid of?

⊷ ═◆═ ⊶

If you had to name one thing that your mate could do to assure that you would leave them forever, what would it be?

⊷ ═◆═ ⊶

If you could eliminate one habit you have, what would you stop doing?

⊷ ═◆═ ⊶

If you just learned that you were to die in exactly one hour, what would you do?

118

If you had to drop a nuclear bomb on one country, where would you drop it?

If you could have witnessed any biblical event, what would you want to have seen?

If you could work for any corporation for which you don't currently work, which would you choose?

If your own ashes were to be kept in an urn, after you die, where would you want the urn kept?

If you could plan the perfect evening out, what would it involve?

If you could program the perfect evening of television shows, which ones would you select, and in what order?

If you had to kill one person you work with, who would you off?

If you had to name the dumbest purchase you've ever made, which would it be?

If you could receive all the products from a single company for free (but could not resell them), which company would you choose?

＊ ⋯ ◼◆◼ ⋯ ＊

If you had to name the one thing that makes you angriest about a relative, what would it be?

＊ ⋯ ◼◆◼ ⋯ ＊

If you were to become the sex slave of one person from history, who would you want it to be?

＊ ⋯ ◼◆◼ ⋯ ＊

If you had to describe the perfect body, what would you say about it?

121

If you could have the autograph of one person from history, who would it be?

If you could have any view from your home, what would it be of?

If you could have asked Richard Nixon one thing, what would you have asked?

If you could have the world's largest collection of one thing, what would it be?

If you could have been the hero from any war, which war would it be, and for what heroic deed?

━━━◆━━━

If you were to inhabit the world of any video or computer game, which one would you select?

━━━◆━━━

If you could leave only one existing book for the world to have five hundred years from now (other than this one), which book would you leave?

If you just learned that tomorrow morning you were to be permanently exiled from your country and could take just three things with you, what would they be?

If you could teach your pet to do one thing, what would it be?

If you could teach your mate to do one thing, what would it be?

If you could write letters to only one person for the rest of your life, who would receive them?

If you were to be reincarnated as someone you know, who would it be?

If you were to be given an acting role in a current TV show, who would you want to play?

If you could arrange for one thing to befall your boss, what would you have happen?

If you could start a new rock band, what would you name it?

If you could have a servant come to your house every day for one hour, what would you have them do?

125

If you were to have your portrait painted, what would you choose as the setting?

If you could choose the very last thing you would see before you die, what would it be?

If you were to be cremated, where would you want your ashes scattered?

If you had to choose your best sexual experience, what would it be?

If you could, in retrospect, thank one teacher you had in school for what they taught you, who would it be, and what would you thank them for?

If you had to pick the worst television series ever made, what would win?

If you could reverse the ongoing extinction of any animal now endangered, which animal would you choose to save?

If you could make a film from any book never produced as a film, what book would you pick?

If you could change one thing to make life easier for your children, what would you do?

———— ≡✦≡ ————

If you had to sell your soul for one thing, what would it be?

———— ≡✦≡ ————

If you could achieve absolute success in only one area of your life, what would you want it to be?

———— ≡✦≡ ————

If you could determine the careers of your children, what would you have them do, assuming they would be successful at it?

128

If you could visit only one more place in the world that you have never been, where would you go for this final voyage?

If you could have anyone locked in a room so that you could torment them for a day, who would you choose, and how would you torment them?

If you had to pick the most difficult question you could be asked, what would it be?

If you could have the answer to any question, what would you ask?

Book 2

$\text{If}^2 \ldots$

If²...

(500 New Questions for the Game of Life)

Evelyn McFarlane & James Saywell
Illustrations by James Saywell

Villard/New York

If ^{2} . . .

The

human imagination is infinite. The fantasies it creates thrill us and uplift us. They even help us to find our way in life. This second collection of "If . . ." questions picks up where its predecessor left off . . . somewhere deep in the extraordinary territory of what people hope for, dream for, and value about each other and themselves.

There is one immediate purpose of these 500 queries: to provoke the mind. Some are humorous, some more serious, and some even quite difficult to answer. Once you begin to play, you may find laughter, tears, revelation, learning, surprise, or contemplation. But you will never lack the potential for fascinating discussions.

As well as the "classic" topics (sex, money, children, death), If^2 . . . includes queries related to issues on the minds of people today, such as welfare, taxes, health care, the environment, and many more. Each of these alone can give rise to further discussion and other questions. Use this book to find out more about your neighbors or your friends; ask "If" questions of your teachers, use them for interviews, call in one to a radio show, send one out on the Internet. Few people can resist engaging in the discussions that "If . . ." initiates. The difficulty with thinking up and compiling these questions was that we were repeatedly interrupted by the irresistible urge to try to answer them, our own imaginations tempting us constantly from the asking, toward the answering. May you, too, give in completely to the same wonderful temptation.

If you found out for certain there is a Heaven and a Hell, how would you change your life?

If you could determine the age at which you will die, but with no guarantees regarding health or money, how old would you like to be when you go?

If you had to select the one thing in life you feel the most guilty about, what would it be?

If you could rid the earth of one thing, what would it be?

5

If you were to close down any charity, which one would you pick?

If you could have overheard a specific conversation between any two people, which would it be?

If you could have the hair of any Hollywood celebrity, whose would you want?

If you had to describe the most memorable night of your life, what would you say?

If you could have the power to hypnotize anyone for a day, who would you pick and what would you have them do?

If you had to name the best album cover ever, which would it be?

If you had to choose the one thing that gives you the most comfort, what would you say?

If you could have witnessed one event from your family's history, what would you want to see?

If you had to choose a single vice president in the history of the United States to become president, who would you pick?

If you had to give up your favorite food forever, what is the minimum amount of money you would demand in return?

If you had to name the best live musical performance you have ever attended, which would you pick?

If you had to name the best speech or presentation you've ever heard, what would it be?

If you had to name the one thing that most frightens you about growing old, what would it be?

If you could be more ambitious in only one aspect of your life, what would it be?

If you could have anyone from history welcome you into the afterlife, who would you want it to be?

If you had to nominate one person you have known for sainthood, who would you choose?

9

If you were to spend the rest of your life in the company of a single type of animal, which would you choose?

If you had to constantly carry a weapon of some kind, what would it be?

— ✠ —

If you could trade your derrière for that of someone else, whose would you want?

— ✠ —

If you had to name the one most important ingredient of human beauty, what would you say it is?

If you had to give a prize for the most sexually attractive politician in U.S. history, who would win it?

If you had to name the single most erotic part of the human body, what would it be?

If you had to name the least erotic part of the human body, what would it be?

If you were to add a thirteenth month to the year, where would you insert it?

11

If you could rid your family of one thing, what would it be?

If you had to name the all-time best song, which would you pick?

If you could say (or have said) one thing to your father on his deathbed, what would it be?

If you could have one thing made out of pure gold, what would you choose?

If you had to pick one experience or situation when you were the most decisive, which would it be?

If you could have only one part of your body massaged every day, what part would you choose?

If you could be the character in any spy novel, who would you choose to be?

If you had to name the time when you came closest to death, when would it have been?

13

If you could make anyone in the world do something each day, who would it be, and what would you have them do?

If you could reverse a single policy of the pope, what would you change?

If you were to choose the breed you would be if you were a dog, which type would best suit you?

If you had to name the one thing that repeatedly makes you angriest, what would it be?

14

If you could organize a family reunion with all of your dead relatives, where would you hold it?

If you could change one thing about the building you work in, what would you alter?

If you were to decide the legal age for sexual consent, what age would it be?

If you were to prescribe a cure for grief, what would it entail?

15

If someone were trying to woo your lover away from you, what methods would bring them the most success?

If you had to name the one thing you have witnessed in your life that best represents Goodness, what would you say?

If you could have modeled in one of Calvin Klein's advertising campaigns for either underwear or fragrance, which ad would you like to have been in?

If you had to name the best music album ever recorded, which would you select?

If you had to name the one time in your life when you were the most angry, when was it?

＊━＊━━◆━━＊━━＊

If you were to be killed by an animal, what kind would you want it to be?

＊━＊━━◆━━＊━━＊

If you were to be tied naked in bed and have your lover melt an ice cube on a single part of your body, without touching you otherwise, where would you want them to melt it?

＊━＊━━◆━━＊━━＊

If you could change one thing about your face to make it more beautiful, what would you alter?

17

If you had to choose the one animal or insect species that is most beautiful, which would you pick?

If you could have any view in the world visible from your bed, what would it be?

If you had to name the most beautiful bed you have ever occupied, what would it be?

If you could exchange work space (e.g., office or cubicle), but not jobs, with someone you presently work with, whose spot would you take?

18

If you could have prevented any single fashion idea or trend from ever happening, which would you have stopped?

If you were to select a moment when you were convinced that an angel was watching over you, when would it have been?

If you could suddenly find out that one work of fiction was actually true, what book would you select?

If you were to have bells ring out loud automatically (for all to hear) every time you did a certain thing, what would it be?

19

If you could have a single button beside your bed that did one thing, what would you want it to do?

If you could have any single kind of appliance attached to your bed, what would it be?

✦

If you were to have Shakespeare to dinner tonight and could invite one other person from history, who would you pick?

✦

If you could have prevented one book from ever having been written, which book would it be?

20

If there were to be one person, among those whom you know, who could from now on read all your thoughts, who would you have it be?

If you had a spot somewhere on your body that, when touched by anyone else, instantly gave you an orgasm, where would you want it to be?

If you could have had one person in your life be less candid with you than they were (or are), who would it be?

If you could have had one person in your life be more candid with you than they were (or are), who would it be?

21

If you had to name a smell that always makes you nostalgic, what would it be?

If you could train a pet bird to do one thing for you and always return home again, what would it do?

⊷ ▆◈▆ ⊶

If you could have been Judge Lance Ito, what one thing would you have done differently?

⊷ ▆◈▆ ⊶

If, in order to save your life, someone you know had to donate their heart to you (without dying), whose heart would you want inside yourself?

If you could have heard the deathbed confession of one person from history, who would you pick?

— ⚜ —

If you were going to die in ten minutes and could confess only one thing in order to pass with peace of mind, what would you say?

— ⚜ —

If you could change places with any of your friends, who would you choose to be?

— ⚜ —

If you could ruin someone's reputation, whose would it be, and how would you do it?

If you could be the house cat or lap dog of any person on earth, whose would you choose to be?

If you could cause any single person to change their mind about one thing or on one topic, who would you pick, and how would you change their thinking?

If you could wake up tomorrow in your own bed, but in another place anywhere in the world inside or outside, where would you like it to be?

If your children could read only four books while growing up, which would you have them read?

If you could eliminate a single kind of danger (other than death) for your children, what would it be?

＊—◄◆►—＊

If you were to pick a city whose character best represents your own personality, which would you choose?

＊—◄◆►—＊

If you could prevent someone you know from overusing one word, who would it be, and what word would it be?

＊—◄◆►—＊

If you could see the inside of any single athlete's locker, whose would it be?

25

If you could have X-ray vision on one person you work with, who would you want it to be?

--- ❖ ---

If you could be more candid with one person you know from now on, who would it be?

--- ❖ ---

If you could have taken better care of one thing in your life, what would it have been?

--- ❖ ---

If you could change one thing about the way you were disciplined as a child, what would you alter?

If you suddenly found the courage to do one thing you have always been afraid of doing, what would you want it to be?

If you had to describe your worst experience with blood, what would you say?

If you were to be the sole confessor of one person on earth, without being able to ever betray their trust no matter what they told you, who would you want it to be?

If you could choose any three songs to compile on a disc to wake up (slowly) to every morning, what would they be, and in what order?

If you could have witnessed the childhood of someone famous, whose would it be?

If you had to exchange wardrobes with someone you know, whose clothes would you want?

＊—＊＋＝＊—＊

If you could have won a single thing you tried for in your life-time but didn't win, what would it be?

＊—＊＋＝＊—＊

If you had to name your greatest conquest in life thus far, what would it be?

28

If you could keep only one book you currently own, which would you choose?

If you could have a set of bed sheets made of anything in the world, what material would you choose?

If you could have known someone as a child that you now know, who would it be?

If you had to name the worst song to wake up to in the morning, what would it be?

If you could commission any living author to write a new book, who would you choose, and what would you have them write about?

If you could have had your mind changed on one issue or decision in your lifetime, what would it have been?

If you could have changed the mind of one person from history on one issue, who and what issue would you pick?

If someone you work with could have X-ray vision on you, who would you most hate it to be?

30

If you were to start an orphanage for children anywhere in the world, where would you want it to be?

If you had to choose the single most charming person you have ever met, who would win?

If just one aspect of your life functioned perfectly forevermore, what would you pick?

If you had to pay one dollar for every time you thought of sex in any form, how long would it be before you went bankrupt?

31

If you could change one thing about the American electoral system, what would it be?

If you could solve one world problem by pledging your own permanent celibacy, what would you do it for?

If you could eliminate one thing other people's children do, what would it be?

If you had to name the most dangerous thing you have ever done on purpose, what would it be?

32

If you came home to find your teenage son or daughter in bed with a postal delivery person, what would you say to them in one sentence?

—·— ≍◆≍ —·—

If you were to be paid to write a new book on any subject you wished, what would it be about?

If you had to eat the cooking of one person you know personally for the rest of your life, whose would you want it to be?

—·— ≍◆≍ —·—

If you were to have three new baby daughters, what would you name them?

If you could give hair back to any balding person you know, who would you pick?

If you found out that there is no afterlife in any sense, how would you change your life?

If you had to name the one thing that really makes your day, what would it be?

If you had to name the one thing that can most readily ruin your day, what would it be?

If you could change one thing about your country's history, what would you alter?

---- ≡◆≡ ----

If you could change one nonphysical thing about your spouse or lover, what would it be?

---- ≡◆≡ ----

If you had to eliminate one emotion from your life, which would it be?

---- ≡◆≡ ----

If you could suddenly be irresistibly charming for one day only, what would you do?

35

If you could give a bronze cast of one part of your body to your most recent ex, what part would it be?

━━◆━━

If you had to identify the one thing destiny probably held in store for you, what would you say it is?

━━◆━━

If you could change one thing about your typical day, what would it be?

━━◆━━

If you discovered a Shakespeare manuscript that no one else had ever seen, what would you do with it?

36

If you could be right behind any single person in line at the Gates of Heaven, who would you choose?

If you found yourself at the Pearly Gates and had one chance to make your case for entry, what would you say?

If you had to name your greatest accomplishment so far in life, what would you say it was?

If you could have back one article of clothing you gave or threw away, what would you want it to be?

If you were to name something that your parents or spouse should have felt guilty about but didn't, what would it be?

If you had to name the most gullible person you know, who is it?

If you could stop loving someone, who would it be?

If you suddenly found yourself at work, wearing women's erotic underwear and nothing else, what would you say (in one sentence) to your fellow workers?

38

If you could enact one law related to royal marriages, what would it say?

If you could give one thing to each of your ex-lovers, what would you give them?

━◆━

If you had to name the person who turned out to be furthest from your first impression of them, who would it be?

━◆━

If you were to name the most clear proof that evil exists in the world, what would you say?

If you could drink only one type of alcoholic drink for the rest of your life, what would you choose?

If you had to fight a duel tomorrow at dawn, and you could determine the type of weapons you both would use, what would they be?

If you could have the vocabulary of any person you know, who would you pick?

If you had to leave everything you own to your alma mater, but you could specify what it would be used for, what would you request?

If you were to name the best "I told you so" you ever got to deliver, what was it?

⋅⋅⋅ ≕✦≕ ⋅⋅⋅

If you were to pick the one thing that always makes you smile, what would it be?

⋅⋅⋅ ≕✦≕ ⋅⋅⋅

If you had to choose the celebrity you most resemble in personality, who would it be?

⋅⋅⋅ ≕✦≕ ⋅⋅⋅

If you were to have two new baby sons, what would you name them?

41

If you had to confess to the most evil thing you have ever done, what would it be?

If you had to name one advantage daughters have over sons, what would you say it is?

If you could cause something that happened in the history of the world to happen again in order to teach something to those in the present, what would you have re-happen?

If you could change places with any celebrity in the world, but would have to remain that person forever, who would you be?

42

If you had to name the nicest thing that has ever happened to you completely by chance, what would it be?

— ⟨⬦⟩ —

If you were to confess to how many people you have honestly been in love with, what would you say?

— ⟨⬦⟩ —

If you wanted your death to have the maximum dramatic effect on people who knew you, how would you choose to die?

If you had to give the same gift to everyone you know next Christmas, what would it be?

If you could touch any single person in the world with only the tip of your index finger, who would you pick, and where would you touch them?

If you had to receive the same (affordable) gift, besides money, from everyone you know on your next birthday, what would you want?

If, in retrospect, you could have been nicer to one person in your life, who would it be?

If you could stop overusing one word in your vocabulary, which word would it be?

44

If you could ask one yes or no question about your own death and have the answer now, what would you ask?

If you could have done one good deed that you had the opportunity to do but didn't, what would it be?

If you had to name the smartest person you have ever met, who would it be?

If you could make one thing come true for one friend, what would it be, and for whom?

45

If you had to identify the time or moment in your life when you felt the most free, when was it?

If you had to name the one personality trait that you have tried the hardest to change in yourself, what would you say?

If you had to name the most gentle person you know, who would it be?

If you could go back for one minute to the Garden of Eden and give Adam advice, what would you say?

46

If you could control the lens of a satellite for one hour, so that you could watch any spot on earth, where would you point it?

—————— ❦ ——————

If you had to name the saddest thing you've ever witnessed, what would it be?

—————— ❦ ——————

If you could have said one thing to Harry Truman the day before he decided to drop the atomic bomb, what would you have said?

—————— ❦ ——————

If you lost feeling everywhere but in one small spot, where would you want the spot to be?

47

If you had to name the thing that most limits your freedom, what would it be?

If you could free yourself from one burden in your life, what would it be?

If you had to name the single best deed a stranger has done for you in your lifetime, what would it be?

If you could get God to do one thing to prove His existence, what would you ask Him to do to convince you?

48

If you could give an Academy Award to the most underappreciated actor in the history of Hollywood, who would you award it to?

⊷ ⊰⊱ ⊷

If you could have changed one thing about your mother's life, what would it be?

⊷ ⊰⊱ ⊷

If you had to name the most difficult good-bye you've ever said, what would it be?

If you could have one free service in your home every day, what would you take?

If you had to describe the silliest thing people do in general, what would you say?

＋・━◆━・＋

If you could guarantee one thing about your next trip, what would it be?

＋・━◆━・＋

If you could completely remove someone's vocal cords for a year, whose would they be?

＋・━◆━・＋

If you had to name the most incredible thing a friend has ever done for you, what would it be?

50

If you were given academic tenure to teach any course you wished at any university in the world, where would you want it to be, and in what subject?

If you had to be buried inside any existing tomb or grave, and the tomb's name would be changed to yours, whose would you want to take over?

＋＋ ＝◆＝ ＋＋

If you could go back and fight any military battle differently, what battle would you pick, and how would you fight it?

＋＋ ＝◆＝ ＋＋

If you had to name the one time when you truly went "beyond the call of duty," when would it be?

If you had to name the physical characteristic of your mate that most resembles their parents, what would it be?

If you could have any number of siblings, how many would you have, and of what gender?

If you had to name the best and worst diets you've ever tried, which would win and which would lose?

If you had to name the most beautiful spot on earth that you've ever seen, what would you choose?

If you had to name the single most important thing in your life, what would it be?

＋・ 〓◆〓 ・＋

If you had to say what one thing in your life best represents your freedom, what would it be?

＋・ 〓◆〓 ・＋

If you had to name the single most important duty of a parent, what would you say it is?

＋・ 〓◆〓 ・＋

If you had to identify what made the best teacher you ever had the best, what would you say it was?

53

If you could gain or lose weight in any one part of your body, where would it be?

— ❈ —

If you could advise one couple you know to separate, who would it be?

If you could have prevented one thing from happening between a friend and yourself, what would it have been?

— ❈ —

If the pope promised he would do one thing you asked of him, what would you ask?

If you had to name the grossest thing you have ever put in your mouth, what would it be?

If God were to whisper one thing in your ear, what would you like Him to say?

If you could do one thing that you've never done with a spray can of Reddi Whip, besides eat it, what would you do and to whom?

If you were to be asked the most difficult thing you can imagine by your best friend, what would it be?

55

If you could have asked Jesus Christ one thing just before the crucifixion, what would it have been?

—— ⚎ ——

If you could repair a relationship with one former friend, who would it be with?

—— ⚎ ——

If you had to predict which famous couple were going to separate next, who would you pick?

If you had to pick the worst driver you know, who would win?

If you asked the most difficult thing you can imagine of your lover, what would it be?

If you had to name the craziest thing you ever did in your youth, what would it be?

If you had to choose the most extreme example of sexual harassment you have suffered, what would it be?

If you could trade in-laws with anyone you know, whose would you take?

57

If you were to pick an object to be worshipped by a new religion, what would it be?

If you could retract one thing you've ever said, what would you take back?

If you could tell any current world leader one thing as president of the United States, what would it be, and to whom would you say it?

If you could ask the greatest sacrifice imaginable of a friend, what would it be?

If you were to identify the most important quality in a friend, what would you say it is?

If you had to pick the biggest Freudian slip you've ever made, what would it be?

If you had to repeat the worst thing you've ever said to your mother, what was it?

If you could have had more time together with someone you know, who would you want it to be with?

59

If you could have the chance to see what has become of one childhood friend, who would you choose to find out about?

If you had to name the single physical characteristic about yourself that most resembles your mother or father, what would it be?

If you had to nominate the best-dressed person you know, who would win?

If you had to name the one thing you envy most about your mate, what would it be?

If you had to name the most violent scene in a movie you have ever seen, what would it be?

If you could have had one thing that one of your friends has, what would you pick, and from whom?

If you could personally see one natural phenomenon that you have never seen, what would it be?

If you had to name the one person your mate knows who makes you jealous, who would it be?

If very good friends were visiting your town, where would you take them to eat if money were no object?

＋・＝◆≡・＋

If you had to name the one thing that most easily makes your mate feel guilty, what would it be?

If you could take revenge on another driver, who would it be, and for what incident?

＋・＝◆≡・＋

If you had to select one movie sequel that was superior to the original, what would it be?

If you could select a role model for each of your kids, who would you pick?

If you could completely redecorate any room in your house at someone else's expense, what room would you choose?

If you could decide how many times a year you saw your own parents, how often would it be?

If you could determine how often you see your in-laws, how often would it be?

If health were not an issue, how many times a month would you exercise?

If you had to describe the worst experience you've had in an automobile, what would it be?

＊－－≡◆≡－－＊

If you had to name the most overrated actor in Hollywood, who would it be?

＊－－≡◆≡－－＊

If you could open and run any kind of restaurant anywhere, what kind of food would you serve, and where?

If you had to name the three most important family values in order of importance, what would they be?

If you could have decided the outcome of the O. J. Simpson trial, what would your verdict be?

If you could have any single Hollywood celebrity be your slave for a weekend, who would you pick?

If you could have any single tabloid story actually come true, which one would it be?

65

If you could give a single piece of advice to the fashion industry right now, what would you say?

If you were on the committee to assign ratings to films, how would you define the categories?

If you could have any single option added to your automobile, what would it be?

If you could have one new store added to your local mall, what would it be?

If you could have prevented the bombing of any single city during a war in this century, which would it be?

⊶ ⚜ ⊷

If you could have participated in any march on Washington, which would you have been part of?

⊶ ⚜ ⊷

If you had known one thing that you didn't when you had your first sexual experience, what would it be?

⊶ ⚜ ⊷

If you had to name the one thing you did as a child to most torment your sibling(s), what was it that you did?

If you could have a lifetime 50 percent discount in any single store at your local mall, which store would it be in?

If you were to have a weekend of sex with a person you would normally consider to be "beneath" you, who would you pick?

If you were to pick the one child you know who you would predict to be the most successful in life, who would it be?

If you could have been present at any one ticker-tape parade, which would you choose?

If you could have a copy of *The New York Times* from any single day in history, which would it be?

If you were Madonna, what would you do for your next publicity stunt?

If you could be given the complete film library of the work of a single actor, who would you pick?

If you could retract one expression of gratitude that you made erroneously, what would you take back?

If you could tell your mother or father one thing that you haven't, what would it be?

If you were invited to the White House for dinner tonight, what would you wear from your current wardrobe?

—✦—

If you had to name one person who should not have divorced their spouse, who would you pick?

—✦—

If you were to become a prostitute, how much money do you think you could charge per hour?

If you had to choose the hour of day when time goes slowest, what would you say?

⚊✦⚊

If you could have your spouse say one thing about you to friends, what would you want him or her to say?

⚊✦⚊

If you had to guess the one thing your mate says about you to friends, what would you say it is?

⚊✦⚊

If you had to identify the most extreme example of ingratitude you can think of from your own experiences, what would it be?

71

If you could freeze your mate's looks at one age, but you would grow older, what age would you pick?

If you had to name the worst thing you've ever done to someone emotionally, what would it be?

If you spoke English with a certain type of American accent other than your own, what would you want it to be?

If you spoke English with a foreign accent, which would you want it to be?

72

If you had to name a song whose lyrics best captured an experience you had, which would it be?

If, from all the people you know, you were to pick a person whose name truly suits them, who would you choose?

If you could take back one gift you have given, but now wish you hadn't, what would it be?

If you could guarantee the happiness of any single person in the world because they most deserve it, who would it be?

If you had to choose the most beautiful name of an existing country, what would you choose?

⊹ ⋯ ≣◊≣ ⋯ ⊹

If you could make someone you know less ignorant about one thing, who would you pick, and what would it be?

If every night you could have one singer appear to serenade you, who would you choose?

⊹ ⋯ ≣◊≣ ⋯ ⊹

If you could learn the total number of hours you have spent in your life doing one thing, what would it be?

If you had to name the person you know with the best attitude regarding money, who would it be?

———— ❖ ————

If you could have only one magazine subscription for life, which would you pick?

———— ❖ ————

If you had to name the biggest hypocrite you have ever met, who would win?

———— ❖ ————

If you could repeat one experience you had with your mate, what would it be?

If you could get a massage every day from one person, from whom would you want it to be?

If you could dedicate a song on the radio right now to your lover or spouse, which song would you pick?

If you had to nominate the worst-dressed person you know, who would it be?

If you had to choose the most necessary thing you do each day, what would you say it was?

If you could pair up any two single people you know, who would you pick?

If you were to decide on a new punishment for convicted murderers, aside from life imprisonment or the death penalty, what would it be?

If you could have your mate surprise you by doing one thing (other than give you a gift), what would you want them to do?

If you could fall asleep each night with your head resting upon anything other than your pillow, what would it be?

If you could choose someone you know to be a guest on a television show, who would it be, and on which show?

If you were to guess which of all the people you know platonically is the best in bed, who would you pick?

If you had to rely on one person you know in any difficult situation, who would you pick?

If you had to work in any store at your local mall, which would it be?

78

If you could have one extra hour each day to do only one thing, what would you do in that hour?

If you had a bust of yourself sculpted, where would you place it?

If you had been Marcia Clark, what one thing would you have done differently in the O. J. Simpson trial?

If your birthday could be in a different month of the year, when would you have it?

If you were to describe an act of true loyalty that you have witnessed, what would it be, and who performed it?

If you could arrange for one thing to happen to your spouse, without them knowing you arranged it, what would you plan?

If you could gain proof of someone's guilt about something, what would it be?

If you could destroy one thing physically, what would it be, and how would you do it?

If the laziest person you know had to do one thing each day for the rest of their life, who would it be, and what would they have to do?

⊷⊶ ≡◆≡ ⊷⊶

If you could teach one person you know a lesson about money, who would it be, and what would they learn?

If you could be more focused in one area of your life, what would it be?

⊷⊶ ≡◆≡ ⊷⊶

If you were to pick the most amoral person you know and teach them a single lesson, who and what would it be?

81

If you could rename every person in your family, what would they each be called?

If you could have the lips of any living person, whose would you want?

If you could avoid any one physical ailment in your old age, what would it be?

If you could throw a great Halloween party anywhere, where would you have it?

If you had to name the best example of fate that you know, what would you say?

If you could touch only one part of your own body for the rest of your life, where would you choose to touch?

If you had to name the book from your childhood that had the biggest influence on you, what book would it be?

If you could punish the most difficult person you work with on a daily basis, what would you do, and to whom?

If you could have your license plate say anything at all, what would it be?

If you had to pick the most beautiful word in your own language, what would you choose?

If you had to describe yourself as a child in one word, what would it be?

If you had to name a single song or album that you most associate with a particular period of your life, what song would you choose, and from what year?

If you had to describe the moment in your life when you had to have the most courage, what would you say?

If you could avoid ever having to see a certain relative again, who would it be?

If you were to describe true generosity by using an example you witnessed, what would you use?

If you had to recount your worst case of putting your foot in your mouth, when was it?

85

If you could go back and express gratitude about one thing in your life, for what would it be, and to whom?

If you were to give an award to someone for being the most moral person, who would win, and what would the award be?

If you were to name the person or people you have the most compassion for, who would it be?

If you could ask your best friend one question you have never had the nerve to ask, what would it be?

86

If you could have kept a detailed diary of one period of your life, so that you could now reread it, what period would it be from?

If you had to name the one situation that would overwhelm your courage, what would it be?

If you were to describe your first kiss, what would you say?

If you devoted the next year to making as much money as possible above all else, how would you do it?

87

If you had to name the most difficult thing about being a teenager today, what would you say?

If you could change one thing about your love life, what would it be?

If you had to name the most embarrassing moment of your life, when was it?

If you could be given a personal tour of any Hollywood celebrity's house, whose would you want to see?

If you had to name the one thing you worried about most in high school, what was it, and did it merit all the fuss?

If you could make one change to your favorite mall, what would it be?

If you could modify your computer in any single way, how would you make it be different?

If you could find the personal diary of one person from history, with all the juicy details, whose would you want to find?

If you could define the legal limitations for pornography, what would you propose?

If you were to name the one possession that means the most to you, what would it be?

If you had to name a person who was the most important role model in your life, who would it be?

If the United States had to sacrifice one state, which one would you give away?

If you could communicate with any type of animal, which would you pick?

If you could have the sense of humor of anyone you know, whose would it be?

＋＋ ＝◆＝ ＋＋

If you had to name a time when you helped a stranger the most, when was it?

＋＋ ＝◆＝ ＋＋

If you had to recall the nicest compliment ever given to you, what would it be?

If you had to name the most difficult period of your life, when would it be?

If you could have a stranger come up to you and whisper anything into your ear, what would you want them to say?

If you could give one piece of advice to the Republican party, what would it be?

If you could implement a strategy to fight the war on drugs, what would it entail?

If you were to decide what legal rights gays and lesbians should have with regard to marriage and children, what would they be?

* * *

If you had to describe your most recurring dream, what would it be?

* * *

If you had to pick one of your personality traits as being the best, which would it be?

If you could havet one more pet, what kind would you get, and what would you name it?

If you had the gift of magic for one day, what would you do?

If you had to name the one thing that has changed the most about growing up since your childhood, what would it be?

If you could pump enormous amounts of money into one area of scientific research, what would it be for?

If you could force someone very rich to give away all their money for a single cause, who would you pick, and what cause would it go to?

94

If a one-year period of your diary were to be published, what year would you want it to be?

--- ✥ ---

If you could have one person you have lost touch with call you up tonight and invite you to dinner, who would you want it to be?

--- ✥ ---

If you had to name the one area of your life that you are the least self-disciplined in, what would it be?

--- ✥ ---

If you could decide exactly how, when, and where your children would learn sex education, what would you consider to be ideal?

If you had to describe the perfect retirement home, what would it be like?

If you had to name the subject you took in school that turned out to be least useful or worthwhile, what would it be?

— ≍✦≍ —

If you could give one piece of advice to the Democratic party, what would it be?

— ≍✦≍ —

If you were asked to define what a feminist is in one sentence, what would your response be?

96

If you could be sainted for doing one thing in life, what would it be for?

If you could change one thing about your marriage, what would you alter?

If you could establish criteria for the right to be a parent, what would they be?

If you could enact one law that applied only to your own family, what would it be?

97

If you could revise the current parole laws, what would you want to do?

If you could have named the first woman something other than Eve, what name would you pick?

If you could have named the first man something other than Adam, what would you pick?

If you could own a single prop from any film ever made, what would you choose?

If you could have done one thing with one of your teachers, what would it be, and with whom?

      ❊

If you could retrieve one toy or stuffed animal from your childhood, which one would you recover?

      ❊

If you could wake up tomorrow in your own bed next to anyone or anything, who or what would it be?

      ❊

If you could do one thing to revise the welfare system, what would you do?

If you had to name a person you know who would be the easiest to seduce, who would it be?

If you were to have the voice of one media personality, whose would it be?

———✺———

If you could have God perform one miracle today, what would you wish it to be?

———✺———

If you could regulate (or deregulate) smoking, what rules would you make (or repeal)?

100

If you could receive more affection from someone you know from now on, who would you want it to be from?

If you could look through anyone's personnel file at work, whose would you pick?

If you had to recall the one time in your childhood or adolescence when you made your parents the most angry, when was it?

If you could reform the health care system right now, how would you do it?

If you had to name the one thing you have done that most pleased your parents, what would you say?

If you had to name the person who most objected to your choice of mate, who would it be?

If you could do one thing right now that isn't being done to help solve the problem of AIDS, what would it be?

If you could own one article of clothing from any film ever made, what would you take?

If you were to sleep with any famous couple, who would you choose?

If you had to name the issue that will be the most important in the next election, what would you say?

If you could have studied one subject in school that you didn't, or that wasn't offered, what would it be?

If you had to have one job that you have had previously, which one would you want again?

103

If you were to name the greatest sexual advantage that women have over men, what would it be?

If your community decided to build low-cost housing, where would you propose it be located?

If you could have the autograph of any athlete you do not have, whose would it be, and what would you like them to sign?

If you could set the guidelines for gun control, what would they be?

If you were given the power to settle the issue of gays in the military, what policy would you set?

----- ❧ -----

If you had to name the best sexual advantage that men have over women, what would it be?

----- ❧ -----

If you could have the original baseball card of any three players in history, who would they be?

----- ❧ -----

If you could relive any single family outing in your life, what would it be?

105

If you had to pick one foreign language that students would be required to learn in school, what would it be?

If you could set the national speed limit for all highways, what would it be?

━━━━━━━━━

If you could sit and have a beer with three sports figures from any time, who would you pick?

━━━━━━━━━

If you could be emotionally closer to one member of your family, who would it be?

106

If you had to pick the member of your family who is least like the others, who would it be?

＊＊＊

If you had to pick the worst teacher from your childhood, who would win the prize?

＊＊＊

If you were to describe your favorite sexual fantasy, what would it be?

＊＊＊

If you were in charge of the military budget, what is the first thing you would do?

If you had to choose the person from your family you most admire, who would it be?

— ▰◆▰ —

If you were six inches tall for a day, what would you do?

— ▰◆▰ —

If you could have anyone in the world stop by for a visit, who would you want it to be?

If the world were to turn to one single source of energy tomorrow, what would you want it to be?

108

If you had to pick the teacher you've had who would be the most disappointed with how your life turned out, who would it be?

If you had to name the world's most pressing environmental concern, what would it be?

If you had to pick the most embarrassing thing your parents did to you as a child, what was it?

If you could have one television sitcom set as your real home, which show would it be from?

109

If you were to have someone's autograph tattooed somewhere on your body, whose would it be, and where would you put it?

+— ≍♦≍ —+

If you could rename any sports team, which would you pick, and what would you rename it?

+— ≍♦≍ —+

If you could add one required course to the present school system, what would it be?

+— ≍♦≍ —+

If you could revise the income tax system, what would you propose?

110

If you could have the personality of any TV character, whose would you adopt?

If you could pass one law to help the environment, what would it be?

~·—◄◆►—·~

If you could retake one course you took in high school or college, which would it be?

~·—◄◆►—·~

If you could make one change to your garden, what would it be?

If you were to set your country's immigration policy, what would it be?

If you were to describe the worst poverty you have ever seen, what would you say?

If you could grow the world's most perfect specimen of plant or flower, what would it be?

If you could impose a heavy luxury tax on any single item, what would it be?

If you could go back to high school to relive one event exactly as it happened, what would you pick?

━━━◆━━━

If you could go back to high school to relive one event as you wish it had been, what would it be?

━━━◆━━━

If you were to name the most ridiculous lawsuit you have ever heard about, what would it be?

━━━◆━━━

If you were to select the person you know who would be the most difficult to seduce, who would you name?

113

If you could spend next New Year's Eve doing anything, what would you do, and with whom?

If you could have been present during the inauguration of any past president, whose would it be?

If you could un-tax anything now currently taxed, what would you pick?

If you could have season tickets for any team, sitting in any place in the stadium, which team would it be and where would you sit?

If you were to spend a week anywhere alone without contact with civilization, where would you go?

If you could ski in any place in the world, where would you go?

⋯ ⧲⧳ ⋯

If you had to choose a television personality to be president of the United States, who would you pick?

⋯ ⧲⧳ ⋯

If you could be caressed by the hands of any person you have known platonically, whose would they be?

115

If you had to name the person you know with the sexiest phone voice, who would win?

—·—✦—·—

If you could relocate your entire workplace to a new location, where would you want it to be?

If you were to be the first lady (or first man), what would you want your role to be?

—·—✦—·—

If you had to be stuck for hours in any airport, which would you want it to be in?

116

If you could spend an entire day in any zoo by yourself, which zoo would you pick to be in, and what would you do?

If you could have an entire city depopulated to explore with a friend for one week, what city would it be, and what would you do?

If you had to recall your worst travel experience, what would it be?

If you had to give up one of your vices for Lent next year, which would you sacrifice?

If you could make one person jealous, who would it be, and how would you do it?

⋯⋯ ☰✦☰ ⋯⋯

If you had to guess that two people at work were having an affair, who would you pair?

If you did not work, how much TV would you watch every day?

⋯⋯ ☰✦☰ ⋯⋯

If you had to pick the TV personality you were most in love with as a kid, who would it be?

118

If you were to make any hotel room your home for a year, where would it be?

If you could live in a past era just so you could wear the clothes in fashion at the time, when would it be?

If you could redesign the uniforms of any sports team, which team would it be, and what changes would you make?

If you could kiss anyone in the world on one spot other than the lips, who would you choose, and where would you kiss them?

119

If you had to name the best speech given at the Academy Awards, whose was it?

If God were to appear before you in any form, what form would you want Him to take?

━━◆━━

If you were to give anyone a raise at work (other than yourself), who would you give it to?

━━◆━━

If you had to name the hardest position to play in sports, what would you say it is?

If you could frame the jockstrap of any sports figure and hang it in your den, whose would you choose?

⊷ ⩻⬧⩺ ⊶

If you had to describe the thing done by someone at work that drives you the craziest, what would you say?

⊷ ⩻⬧⩺ ⊶

If you had to name the next person who should be fired at your place of employment, who would you choose?

⊷ ⩻⬧⩺ ⊶

If you were to name one person you know who is a true gentle-man, who would it be?

If you were to define the word *courage* by giving an example, how would you do it?

⋯⋯ ⚞✦⚟ ⋯⋯

If you had to pick the one institution you have the most faith in, what would you say?

⋯⋯ ⚞✦⚟ ⋯⋯

If you were to be the opposite sex for a single day, what would you do?

⋯⋯ ⚞✦⚟ ⋯⋯

If you could play a prank on anyone at work with impunity, what would you do, and to whom?

122

If you could go back to one place you have been in your life, where would you go?

If you had to be addicted to one thing, what would it be?

———— ❦ ————

If you were to have the hands of someone you know, whose would you want?

———— ❦ ————

If you could remove the ability to hate from one person in the world today, who would it be?

123

If you could be any sign of the zodiac other than your own, what would you want to be?

If you could run any existing charity, which would it be?

If you could insist that one person you work with deliver coffee to you every day, who would you chose?

If you could have taken part in any single historical ceremony, what would it have been?

124

If you were to name the one choice in life that you would never want to make again, what would it be?

If you had to disguise yourself physically, how would you do it?

If you could have one science fiction story come true, which would it be?

If you had to have the hair of a current politician, whose would you pick?

125

If you could remove one marking from your skin, which one would it be?

If you had to choose, from among your current friends, one person to be your partner in a new business venture, who would you choose?

If you were to name the most obnoxious tourists you've encountered, who would they be?

If you had to eliminate forever one form of weather, what would it be?

126

If you could go back to an incident in your past, in order to act more honorably than you did, what situation would it be?

If you could gain back all the hours you've spent in your life doing a certain thing, what would it be?

If you could have one piece of jewelry belonging to someone you know personally, what would you pick?

If you could ensure one thing about Heaven besides its existence, what would it be?

If you were to get a divorce, what is the one thing you would fight for above all else (besides your children)?

·—· ✠✦✠ —·

If you could have had any job in history, what would it have been?

·—· ✠✦✠ —·

If you could ensure that one existing law would never be broken by anyone, which would it be?

·—· ✠✦✠ —·

If you could go back in time to undo one injury you inflicted on someone else, what would it be?

128

If you had to name the one person you have been most jealous of, who would win?

If you had to name the one thing about your life right now that you would not change, what would it be?

If you could receive a kiss from anyone in the world on one part of your body other than your lips, who would you want to kiss you, and where?

If you could forget one thing, what would it be?